The Institution of Civil Engineers

The Engineering and Construction Contract
Option F

An NEC document

A form of contract for
a management contract

Thomas Telford, London

Published for the Institution of Civil Engineers by Thomas Telford Services Ltd, Thomas Telford House, 1 Heron Quay, London E14 4JD

The NEC System is published as a series of documents of which this is one.

ISBN (series) 0 7277 2081 3

ISBN (this document) 0 7277 2077 5

Consultative edition 1991
First edition 1993
Second edition November 1995

British Library Cataloguing in Publication Data for this publication is available from the British Library.

Printed and bound in Great Britain by Staples Printers Rochester Ltd, Rochester, Kent.

CONTENTS

In this contract the core clauses are the ECC core clauses and the clauses set out in the ECC as main option clauses: Option F. The latter are included in sequence and are printed in **bold type** in this contract.

ACKNOWLEDGEMENTS

The New Engineering Contract has been produced by the Institution of Civil Engineers through its New Engineering Contract Working Group.

The New Engineering Contract has been designed and drafted by Dr Martin Barnes of Coopers and Lybrand with the assistance of Professor J. G. Perry of The University of Birmingham, T. W. Weddell of Travers Morgan Management, T. H. Nicholson, Consultant to the Institution of Civil Engineers, A. Norman of the University of Manchester Institute of Science and Technology and P. A. Baird, Corporate Contracts Consultant, Eskom, South Africa.

The members of the New Engineering Contract Working Group are

    R. L. Wilson, CBE, BSc(Eng), FEng, FICE (Chairman)
    M. W. Abrahamson, BA, LLB, FCIArb
    P. A. Baird, BSc, CEng, FICE, M(SA)ICE, MAPM
    M. Barnes, BSc(Eng), PhD, FEng, FICE, FCIOB, CBIM, FAPM, FInstCES, ACIArb
    J. A. Chandler, MA, CEng, FICE, FCIArb
    L. T. Eames, BSc, FRICS, MCIOB
    F. Griffiths, CEng, FIEE, FICE, FCIPS, FInstM, MAPM
    J. Halliday, CEng, MICE
    K. Lumb, FRICS, ACIArb
    W. S. McAlonan, MSc, FEng, FICE, FIHT
    T. H. Nicholson, BSc, CEng, FICE (Secretary)
    A. Norman, BSc, MSc, CEng, MICE, MAPM
    Professor J. G. Perry, MEng, PhD, CEng, MICE, MAPM
    T. W. Weddell, BSc, CEng, DIC, FICE, FIStructE, ACIArb

    I. M. H. Moore, CBE (Director External Affairs, ICE)
    J. J. Lewis (Project Manager, June 1991 – January 1992)
    R. F. Bell, BSc, CEng, FICE (Project Manager from January 1992)

The Institution of Civil Engineers also acknowledges the considerable contributions made to the New Engineering Contract by

    N. G. Bunni, BSc, MSc, PhD, CEng, FIEI, FICE, FCIArb
    S. C. McCarthy, BE, MSc, PhD, MIEI

The 2nd edition of the NEC documents for engineering and construction contracts were produced by the Institution of Civil Engineers through its New Engineering Contract Panel.

The members of the New Engineering Contract Panel are:

    M. Barnes (Chairman), BSc(Eng), PhD, FEng, FICE, FCIOB, CIMgt, MBCS, FRSA, FAPM, FInstCES, ACIArb
    P. A. Baird, BSc, CEng, FICE, M(SA)ICE, MAPM
    L. T. Eames, BSc, FRICS, MCIOB
    T. H. Nicholson (Secretary), BSc, CEng, FICE
    M. A. Noakes, BSc, CEng, MICE, MIWEM
    Professor J. G. Perry, MEng, PhD, CEng, FICE, MAPM
    N. C. Shaw, FCIPS, CEng, MIMechE
    T. W. Weddell, BSc, CEng, DIC, FICE, FIStructE, ACIArb

The Institution of Civil Engineers also acknowledges the help in preparing the second edition given by many other people and, in particular, by:

J. C. Broome BEng
Professor P. N. Capper
G. C. Dixon MA
D. P. Maidment ACII
A. Norman, BSc, MSc, CEng, MICE, MAPM

SCHEDULE OF OPTIONS

The following secondary options should be considered. It is not necessary to use any of them. Any combination may be used.

Option G	Performance bond
Option H	Parent company guarantee
Option J	Advanced payment to the *Contractor*
Option L	Sectional Completion
Option M	Limitation of the *Contractor*'s liability for his design to reasonable skill and care
Option Q	Bonus for early Completion
Option R	Delay damages
Option S	Low performance damages
Option T	Changes in the law
Option U	The Construction (Design and Management) Regulations 1994 (to be used for contracts in the UK)
Option V	Trust Fund
Option Z	Additional conditions of contract

THE NEC ENGINEERING AND CONSTRUCTION CONTRACT

CORE CLAUSES

1 General

Actions **10**

10.1 The *Employer*, the *Contractor*, the *Project Manager* and the *Supervisor* shall act as stated in this contract and in a spirit of mutual trust and co-operation. The *Adjudicator* shall act as stated in this contract and in a spirit of independence.

Identified and defined terms **11**

11.1 In these conditions of contract, terms identified in the Contract Data are in italics and defined terms have capital initials.

11.2 (1) The Parties are the *Employer* and the *Contractor*.

(2) Others are people or organisations who are not the *Employer,* the *Project Manager,* the *Supervisor,* the *Adjudicator*, the *Contractor*, or any employee, Subcontractor or supplier of the *Contractor*.

(3) The Contract Date is the date when this contract came into existence.

(4) To Provide the Works means to do the work necessary to complete the *works* in accordance with this contract and all incidental work, services and actions which this contract requires.

(5) Works Information is information which either

- specifies and describes the *works* or
- states any constraints on how the *Contractor* Provides the Works

and is either

- in the documents which the Contract Data states it is in or
- in an instruction given in accordance with this contract.

(6) Site Information is information which

- describes the Site and its surroundings and
- is in the documents which the Contract Data states it is in.

(7) The Site is the area within the *boundaries of the site* and the volumes above and below it which are affected by work included in this contract.

(8) The Working Areas are the *working areas* unless later changed in accordance with this contract.

(9) A Subcontractor is a person or corporate body who has a contract with the *Contractor* to provide part of the *works* or to supply Plant and Materials which he has wholly or partly designed specifically for the *works*.

(10) Plant and Materials are items intended to be included in the *works*.

(11) Equipment is items provided by the *Contractor* and used by him to Provide the Works and which the Works Information does not require him to include in the *works*.

(12) The Completion Date is the *completion date* unless later changed in accordance with this contract.

(13) Completion is when the *Contractor* has

- done all the work which the Works Information states he is to do by the Completion Date and
- corrected notified Defects which would have prevented the *Employer* from using the *works*.

(14) The Accepted Programme is the programme identified in the Contract Data or is the latest programme accepted by the *Project Manager*. The latest programme accepted by the *Project Manager* supersedes previous Accepted Programmes.

(15) A Defect is

- a part of the *works* which is not in accordance with the Works Information or
- a part of the *works* designed by the *Contractor* which is not in accordance with

  - the applicable law or
  - the *Contractor*'s design which has been accepted by the *Project Manager*.

(16) The Defects Certificate is either a list of Defects that the *Supervisor* has notified before the *defects date* which the *Contractor* has not corrected or, if there are no such Defects, a statement that there are none.

(17) The Fee is the amount calculated by applying the *fee percentage* to the amount of Actual Cost.

(19) The Prices are the Actual Cost plus the Fee.

(22) The Price for Work Done to Date is the amount of Actual Cost which the *Contractor* has accepted for payment plus the Fee.

(26) Actual Cost is the amount of payments due to Subcontractors for work which the *Contractor* is required to subcontract, less any Disallowed Cost.

(29) Disallowed Cost is cost which the *Project Manager* decides

- **is not justified by the accounts and records provided by the *Contractor*,**
- **should not have been paid to a Subcontractor in accordance with his subcontract,**
- **was incurred only because the *Contractor* did not**

  - **follow an acceptance or procurement procedure stated in the Works Information or**
  - **give an early warning which he could have given or**

- **results from paying a Subcontractor more for a compensation event than is included in the accepted quotation or assessment for the compensation event.**

Interpretation and the Law	**12**	
	12.1	In this contract, except where the context shows otherwise, words in the singular also mean in the plural and the other way round and words in the masculine also mean in the feminine and neuter.
	12.2	This contract is governed by the *law of the contract*.

Communications	**13**	
	13.1	Each instruction, certificate, submission, proposal, record, acceptance, notification and reply which this contract requires is communicated in a form which can be read, copied and recorded. Writing is in the *language of this contract*.
	13.2	A communication has effect when it is received at the last address notified by the recipient for receiving communications or, if none is notified, at the address of the recipient stated in the Contract Data.
	13.3	If this contract requires the *Project Manager*, the *Supervisor* or the *Contractor* to reply to a communication, unless otherwise stated in this contract, he replies within the *period for reply*.
	13.4	The *Project Manager* replies to a communication submitted or resubmitted to him by the *Contractor* for acceptance. If his reply is not acceptance, he states his reasons and the *Contractor* resubmits the communication within the *period for reply* taking account of these reasons. A reason for withholding acceptance is that more information is needed in order to assess the *Contractor*'s submission fully.
	13.5	The *Project Manager* may extend the *period for reply* to a communication if the *Project Manager* and the *Contractor* agree to the extension before the reply is due. The *Project Manager* notifies the extension which has been agreed to the *Contractor*.
	13.6	The *Project Manager* issues his certificates to the *Employer* and the *Contractor*. The *Supervisor* issues his certificates to the *Project Manager* and the *Contractor*.
	13.7	A notification which this contract requires is communicated separately from other communications.
	13.8	The *Project Manager* may withold acceptance of a submission by the *Contractor*. Witholding acceptance for a reason stated in this contract is not a compensation event.

The *Project Manager* and the *Supervisor*	**14**	
	14.1	The *Project Manager*'s or the *Supervisor*'s acceptance of a communication from the *Contractor* or of his work does not change the *Contractor*'s responsibility to Provide the Works or his liability for his design.
	14.2	The *Project Manager* and the *Supervisor*, after notifying the *Contractor*, may delegate any of their actions and may cancel any delegation. A reference to an action of the *Project Manager* or the *Supervisor* in this contract includes an action by his delegate.
	14.3	The *Project Manager* may give an instruction to the *Contractor* which changes the Works Information.
	14.4	The *Employer* may replace the *Project Manager* or the *Supervisor* after he has notified the *Contractor* of the name of the replacement.

Adding to the *working areas*	**15**	
	15.1	The *Contractor* may submit a proposal for adding to the Working Areas to the *Project Manager* for acceptance. A reason for not accepting is that

- the proposed addition is not necessary for Providing the Works or
- the proposed area will be used for work not in this contract.

Early warning 16

16.1 The *Contractor* and the *Project Manager* give an early warning by notifying the other as soon as either becomes aware of any matter which could

- increase the total of the Prices,
- delay Completion or
- impair the performance of the *works* in use.

16.2 Either the *Project Manager* or the *Contractor* may instruct the other to attend an early warning meeting. Each may instruct other people to attend if the other agrees.

16.3 At an early warning meeting those who attend co-operate in

- making and considering proposals for how the effect of each matter which has been notified as an early warning can be avoided or reduced,
- seeking solutions that will bring advantage to all those who will be affected and
- deciding upon actions which they will take and who, in accordance with this contract, will take them.

16.4 The *Project Manager* records the proposals considered and the decisions taken at an early warning meeting and gives a copy of his record to the *Contractor*.

**Ambiguities and 17
inconsistencies**

17.1 The *Project Manager* or the *Contractor* notifies the other as soon as either becomes aware of an ambiguity or inconsistency in or between the documents which are part of this contract. The *Project Manager* gives an instruction resolving the ambiguity or inconsistency.

Health and safety 18

18.1 The *Contractor* acts in accordance with the health and safety requirements stated in the Works Information.

**Illegal and impossible 19
requirements**

19.1 The *Contractor* notifies the *Project Manager* as soon as he becomes aware that the Works Information requires him to do anything which is illegal or impossible. If the *Project Manager* agrees, he gives an instruction to change the Works Information appropriately.

2 The *Contractor*'s main responsibilities

Providing the Works   **20**

20.1   The *Contractor* Provides the Works in accordance with the Works Information.

20.2   **The *Contractor* manages the *Contractor*'s design and the construction and installation of the works. The *Contractor* subcontracts design, construction and installation of the *works* and other work which is stated in the Works Information as to be subcontracted. He either does other work which is not stated in the Works Information as to be subcontracted himself or subcontracts it.**

20.3   **The *Contractor* advises the *Project Manager* on the practical implications of the design of the *works* and on subcontracting arrangements.**

20.4   **The *Contractor* prepares forecasts of the total Actual Cost for the whole of the *works* in consultation with the *Project Manager* and submits them to the *Project Manager*. Forecasts are prepared at the intervals stated in the Contract Data from the *starting date* until Completion of the whole of the *works*. An explanation of the changes made since the previous forecast is submitted with each forecast.**

The *Contractor*'s design   **21**

21.1   The *Contractor* designs the parts of the *works* which the Works Information states he is to design.

21.2   The *Contractor* submits the particulars of his design as the Works Information requires to the *Project Manager* for acceptance. A reason for not accepting the *Contractor*'s design is that

- it does not comply with the Works Information or
- it does not comply with the applicable law.

The *Contractor* does not proceed with the relevant work until the *Project Manager* has accepted his design.

21.3   The *Contractor* may submit his design for acceptance in parts if the design of each part can be assessed fully.

21.4   The *Contractor* indemnifies the *Employer* against claims, compensation and costs due to the *Contractor* infringing a patent or copyright.

21.5   The *Contractor*'s liability to the *Employer* for Defects due to his design that are not listed on the Defects Certificate is limited to the amount stated in the Contract Data in addition to any damages stated in this contract for delay or low performance.

Using the *Contractor*'s design   **22**

22.1   The *Employer* may use and copy the *Contractor*'s design for any purpose connected with construction, use, alteration or demolition of the *works* unless otherwise stated in the Works Information and for other purposes as stated in the Works Information.

Design of Equipment   **23**

23.1   The *Contractor* submits particulars of the design of an item of Equipment to the *Project Manager* for acceptance if the *Project Manager* instructs him to. A reason for not accepting is that the design of the item will not allow the *Contractor* to Provide the Works in accordance with

- the Works Information,
- the *Contractor*'s design which the *Project Manager* has accepted or
- the applicable law.

People **24**

24.1   The *Contractor* either employs each key person named to do the job for him stated in the Contract Data or employs a replacement person who has been accepted by the *Project Manager*. The *Contractor* submits the name, relevant qualifications and experience of a proposed replacement person to the *Project Manager* for acceptance. A reason for not accepting the person is that his relevant qualifications and experience are not as good as those of the person who is to be replaced.

24.2   The *Project Manager* may, having stated his reasons, instruct the *Contractor* to remove an employee. The *Contractor* then arranges that, after one day, the employee has no further connection with the work included in this contract.

Co-operation **25**

25.1   The *Contractor* co-operates with Others in obtaining and providing information which they need in connection with the *works*. He shares the Working Areas with Others as stated in the Works Information.

Subcontracting **26**

26.1   If the *Contractor* subcontracts work, he is responsible for performing this contract as if he had not subcontracted. This contract applies as if a Subcontractor's employees and equipment were the *Contractor*'s.

26.2   The *Contractor* submits the name of each proposed Subcontractor to the *Project Manager* for acceptance. A reason for not accepting the Subcontractor is that his appointment will not allow the *Contractor* to Provide the Works. The *Contractor* does not appoint a proposed Subcontractor until the *Project Manager* has accepted him.

26.3   The *Contractor* submits the proposed conditions of contract for each subcontract to the *Project Manager* for acceptance unless

- the NEC Engineering and Construction Subcontract or the NEC Professional Services Contract is to be used or
- the *Project Manager* has agreed that no submission is required.

The *Contractor* does not appoint a Subcontractor on the proposed subcontract conditions submitted until the *Project Manager* has accepted them. A reason for not accepting them is that

- they will not allow the *Contractor* to Provide the Works or
- they do not include a statement that the parties to the subcontract shall act in a spirit of mutual trust and co-operation.

26.4   **The *Contractor* submits the proposed contract data for each subcontract for acceptance to the *Project Manager* if**

- **the NEC Engineering and Construction Subcontract or the NEC Professional Services Contract is to be used and**
- **the *Project Manager* instructs the *Contractor* to make the submission.**

A reason for not accepting the proposed contract data is that its use will not allow the *Contractor* to Provide the Works.

Approval from Others **27**

27.1   The *Contractor* obtains approval of his design from Others where necessary.

Access to the work 28

28.1   The *Contractor* provides access to work being done and to Plant and Materials being stored for this contract for

- the *Project Manager*,
- the *Supervisor* and
- others notified to him by the *Project Manager*.

Instructions 29

29.1   The *Contractor* obeys an instruction which is in accordance with this contract and is given to him by the *Project Manager* or the *Supervisor*.

3 Time

Starting and Completion **30**

30.1 The *Contractor* does not start work on the Site until the first *possession date* and does the work so that Completion is on or before the Completion Date.

30.2 The *Project Manager* decides the date of Completion. The *Project Manager* certifies Completion within one week of Completion.

The programme **31**

31.1 If a programme is not identified in the Contract Data, the *Contractor* submits a first programme to the *Project Manager* for acceptance within the period stated in the Contract Data.

31.2 The *Contractor* shows on each programme which he submits for acceptance

- the *starting date*, *possession dates* and Completion Date,
- for each operation, a method statement which identifies the Equipment and other resources which the *Contractor* plans to use,
- planned Completion,
- the order and timing of

  - the operations which the *Contractor* plans to do in order to Provide the Works and
  - the work of the *Employer* and Others either as stated in the Works Information or as later agreed with them by the *Contractor*,

- the dates when the *Contractor* plans to complete work needed to allow the *Employer* and Others to do their work,

- provisions for

  - float,
  - time risk allowances,
  - health and safety requirements and
  - the procedures set out in this contract,

- the dates when, in order to Provide the Works in accordance with his programme, the *Contractor* will need

  - possession of a part of the Site if later than its *possession date*,
  - acceptances and
  - Plant and Materials and other things to be provided by the *Employer* and

- other information which the Works Information requires the *Contractor* to show on a programme submitted for acceptance.

31.3 Within two weeks of the *Contractor* submitting a programme to him for acceptance, the *Project Manager* either accepts the programme or notifies the *Contractor* of his reasons for not accepting it. A reason for not accepting a programme is that

- the *Contractor*'s plans which it shows are not practicable,
- it does not show the information which this contract requires,
- it does not represent the *Contractor*'s plans realistically or
- it does not comply with the Works Information.

Revising the programme **32**

32.1   The *Contractor* shows on each revised programme

- the actual progress achieved on each operation and its effect upon the timing of the remaining work,
- the effects of implemented compensation events and of notified early warning matters,
- how the *Contractor* plans to deal with any delays and to correct notified Defects and
- any other changes which the *Contractor* proposes to make to the Accepted Programme.

32.2   The *Contractor* submits a revised programme to the *Project Manager* for acceptance

- within the *period for reply* after the *Project Manager* has instructed him to,
- when the *Contractor* chooses to and, in any case,
- at no longer interval than the interval stated in the Contract Data from the *starting date* until Completion of the whole of the *works*.

Possession of the Site **33**

33.1   The *Employer* gives possession of each part of the Site to the *Contractor* on or before the later of its *possession date* and the date for possession shown on the Accepted Programme.

33.2   While the *Contractor* has possession of a part of the Site, the *Employer* gives the *Contractor* access to and use of it and the *Employer* and the *Contractor* provide facilities and services as stated in the Works Information. Any cost incurred by the *Employer* as a result of the *Contractor* not providing the facilities and services he is to provide is assessed by the *Project Manager* and paid by the *Contractor*.

Instructions to stop or not **34**
to start work 34.1   The *Project Manager* may instruct the *Contractor* to stop or not to start any work and may later instruct him that he may re-start or start it.

Take over **35**

35.1   Possession of each part of the Site returns to the *Employer* when he takes over the part of the *works* which occupies it. Possession of the whole Site returns to the *Employer* when the *Project Manager* certifies termination.

35.2   The *Employer* need not take over the *works* before the Completion Date if it is stated in the Contract Data that he is not willing to do so. Otherwise the *Employer* takes over the *works* not more than two weeks after Completion.

35.3   The *Employer* may use any part of the *works* before Completion has been certified. If he does so, he takes over the part of the *works* when he begins to use it except if the use is

- for a reason stated in the Works Information or
- to suit the *Contractor*'s method of working.

35.4   The *Project Manager* certifies the date upon which the *Employer* takes over any part of the *works* and its extent within one week of the date.

Acceleration **36**

36.1   The *Project Manager* may instruct the *Contractor* to submit a quotation for an acceleration to achieve Completion before the Completion Date. A quotation for an acceleration comprises proposed changes to the Prices and the Completion Date and a revised programme.

36.2   The *Contractor* submits a quotation or gives his reasons for not doing so within the *period for reply*.

36.4   When the *Project Manager* accepts a quotation for an acceleration, he changes the Completion Date accordingly and accepts the revised programme.

36.5   The *Contractor* submits a Subcontractor's proposal to accelerate to the *Project Manager* for acceptance.

4 Testing and Defects

Tests and inspections **40**

40.1 This clause only governs tests and inspections required by the Works Information and the applicable law.

40.2 The *Contractor* and the *Employer* provide materials, facilities and samples for tests and inspections as stated in the Works Information.

40.3 The *Contractor* and the *Supervisor* each notifies the other of each of his tests and inspections before it starts and afterwards notifies the other of its results. The *Contractor* notifies the *Supervisor* in time for a test or inspection to be arranged and done before doing work which would obstruct the test or inspection. The *Supervisor* may watch any test done by the *Contractor*.

40.4 If a test or inspection shows that any work has a Defect, the *Contractor* corrects the Defect and the test or inspection is repeated.

40.5 The *Supervisor* does his tests and inspections without causing unnecessary delay to the work or to a payment which is conditional upon a test or inspection being successful. A payment which is conditional upon a *Supervisor*'s test or inspection being successful becomes due at the later of the *defects date* and the end of the last *defect correction period* if

- the *Supervisor* has not done the test or inspection and
- the delay to the test or inspection is not the *Contractor*'s fault.

40.6 The *Project Manager* assesses the cost incurred by the *Employer* in repeating a test or inspection after a Defect is found. The *Contractor* pays the amount assessed.

Testing and inspection **41**
before delivery 41.1 The *Contractor* does not bring to the Working Areas those Plant and Materials which the Works Information states are to be tested or inspected before delivery until the *Supervisor* has notified the *Contractor* that they have passed the test or inspection.

Searching and notifying **42**
Defects 42.1 The *Supervisor* may instruct the *Contractor* to search. He gives his reason for the search with his instruction. Searching may include

- uncovering, dismantling, re-covering and re-erecting work,
- providing facilities, materials and samples for tests and inspections done by the *Supervisor* and
- doing tests and inspections which the Works Information does not require.

42.2 Until the *defects date,* the *Supervisor* notifies the *Contractor* of each Defect which he finds and the *Contractor* notifies the *Supervisor* of each Defect which he finds.

Correcting Defects **43**

43.1 The *Contractor* corrects Defects whether or not the *Supervisor* notifies him of them. The *Contractor* corrects notified Defects before the end of the *defect correction period*. This period begins at Completion for Defects notified before Completion and when the Defect is notified for other Defects.

43.2 The *Supervisor* issues the Defects Certificate at the later of the *defects date* and the end of the last *defect correction period*.

43.3 The *Project Manager* arranges for the *Employer* to give access to and use of any part of the *works* which he has taken over to the *Contractor* if it is needed for correcting a Defect. If the *Project Manager* has not arranged suitable access and use within the *defect correction period*, he extends the period for correcting the Defect as necessary.

Accepting Defects **44**

44.1 The *Contractor* and the *Project Manager* may each propose to the other that the Works Information should be changed so that a Defect does not have to be corrected.

44.2 If the *Contractor* and the *Project Manager* are prepared to consider the change, the *Contractor* submits a quotation for reduced Prices or an earlier Completion Date or both to the *Project Manager* for acceptance. If the *Project Manager* accepts the quotation, he gives an instruction to change the Works Information, the Prices and the Completion Date accordingly.

Uncorrected Defects **45**

45.1 If the *Contractor* has not corrected a notified Defect within its *defect correction period*, the *Project Manager* assesses the cost of having the Defect corrected by other people and the *Contractor* pays this amount.

5 Payment

Assessing the amount due   **50**

50.1   The *Project Manager* assesses the amount due at each assessment date. The first assessment date is decided by the *Project Manager* to suit the procedures of the Parties and is not later than the *assessment interval* after the *starting date*. Later assessment dates occur

- at the end of each *assessment interval* until Completion of the whole of the *works*,
- at Completion of the whole of the works,
- four weeks after the Supervisor issues the Defects Certificate and
- after Completion of the whole of the *works*,

  - when an amount due is corrected and
  - when a payment is made late.

50.2   The amount due is the Price for Work Done to Date plus other amounts to be paid to the *Contractor* less amounts to be paid by or retained from the *Contractor*. Any value added tax or sales tax which the law requires the *Employer* to pay to the *Contractor* is included in the amount due.

50.3   If no programme is identified in the Contract Data, one quarter of the Price for Work Done to Date is retained in assessments of the amount due until the *Contractor* has submitted a first programme to the *Project Manager* for acceptance showing the information which this contract requires.

50.4   In assessing the amount due, the *Project Manager* considers any application for payment the *Contractor* has submitted on or before the assessment date. The *Project Manager* gives the *Contractor* details of how the amount due has been assessed.

50.5   The *Project Manager* corrects any wrongly assessed amount due in a later payment certificate.

50.7   Payments of Actual Cost made by the *Contractor* in a currency other than the *currency of this contract* are included in the amount due as payments to be made to him in the same currency. Such payments are converted to the *currency of this contract* in order to calculate the Fee at the *exchange rates*.

Payment   **51**

51.1   The *Project Manager* certifies a payment within one week of each assessment date. The first payment is the amount due. Other payments are the change in the amount due since the last payment certificate. A payment is made by the *Contractor* to the *Employer* if the change reduces the amount due. Other payments are made by the *Employer* to the *Contractor*. Payments are in the *currency of this contract* unless otherwise stated in this contract.

51.2   Each certified payment is made within three weeks of the assessment date or, if a different period is stated in the Contract Data, within the period stated. If a payment is late, interest is paid on the late payment. Interest is assessed from the date by which the late payment should have been made until the date when the late payment is made, and is included in the first assessment after the late payment is made.

51.3 If an amount due is corrected in a later certificate either

- by the *Project Manager,* whether in relation to a mistake or a compensation event, or
- following a decision of the *Adjudicator* or the *tribunal,*

interest on the correcting amount is paid. Interest is assessed from the date when the incorrect amount was certified until the date when the correcting amount is certified and is included in the assessment which includes the correcting amount.

51.4 If the *Project Manager* does not issue a certificate which he should issue, interest is paid on the amount which he should have certified. Interest is assessed from the date by which he should have certified the amount until the date when he certifies the amount and is included in the amount then certified.

51.5 Interest is calculated at the *interest rate* and is compounded annually.

Actual Cost **52**

52.1 All the *Contractor*'s costs which are not included in the Actual Cost are deemed to be included in the *fee percentage.* Amounts included in Actual Cost are at open market or competitively tendered prices with all discounts, rebates and taxes which can be recovered deducted.

52.2 **The *Contractor* keeps**

- **accounts of his payments of Actual Cost,**
- **records which show that the payments have been made,**
- **records of communications and calculations relating to assessment of compensation events for Subcontractors and**
- **other accounts and records as stated in the Works Information.**

52.3 **The *Contractor* allows the *Project Manager* to inspect at any time within working hours the accounts and records which he is required to keep.**

6 Compensation events

Compensation events 60

60.1 The following are compensation events.

(1) The *Project Manager* gives an instruction changing the Works Information except

- a change made in order to accept a Defect or
- a change to the Works Information provided by the *Contractor* for his design which is made at his request or to comply with other Works Information provided by the *Employer*.

(2) The *Employer* does not give possession of a part of the Site by the later of its *possession date* and the date required by the Accepted Programme.

(3) The *Employer* does not provide something which he is to provide by the date for providing it required by the Accepted Programme.

(4) The *Project Manager* gives an instruction to stop or not to start any work.

(5) The *Employer* or Others do not work within the times shown on the Accepted Programme or do not work within the conditions stated in the Works Information.

(6) The *Project Manager* or the *Supervisor* does not reply to a communication from the *Contractor* within the period required by this contract.

(7) The *Project Manager* gives an instruction for dealing with an object of value or of historical or other interest found within the Site.

(8) The *Project Manager* or the *Supervisor* changes a decision which he has previously communicated to the *Contractor*.

(9) The *Project Manager* withholds an acceptance (other than acceptance of a quotation for acceleration or for not correcting a Defect) for a reason not stated in this contract.

(10) The *Supervisor* instructs the *Contractor* to search and no Defect is found unless the search is needed only because the *Contractor* gave insufficient notice of doing work obstructing a required test or inspection.

(11) A test or inspection done by the *Supervisor* causes unnecessary delay.

(12) The *Contractor* encounters physical conditions which

- are within the Site,
- are not weather conditions and
- which an experienced contractor would have judged at the Contract Date to have such a small chance of occurring that it would have been unreasonable for him to have allowed for them.

(13) A *weather measurement* is recorded

- within a calendar month,
- before the Completion Date for the whole of the *works* and
- at the place stated in the Contract Data

the value of which, by comparison with the *weather data*, is shown to occur on average less frequently than once in ten years.

(14) An *Employer*'s risk event occurs.

(15) The *Project Manager* certifies take over of a part of the *works* before both Completion and the Completion Date.

(16) The *Employer* does not provide materials, facilities and samples for tests as stated in the Works Information.

(17) The *Project Manager* notifies a correction to an assumption about the nature of a compensation event.

(18) A breach of contract by the *Employer* which is not one of the other compensation events in this contract.

60.2 In judging the physical conditions, the *Contractor* is assumed to have taken into account

- the Site Information,
- publicly available information referred to in the Site Information,
- information obtainable from a visual inspection of the Site and
- other information which an experienced contractor could reasonably be expected to have or to obtain.

60.3 If there is an inconsistency within the Site Information (including the information referred to in it), the *Contractor* is assumed to have taken into account the physical conditions more favourable to doing the work.

Notifying compensation **61**
events 61.1 For compensation events which arise from the *Project Manager* or the *Supervisor* giving an instruction or changing an earlier decision, the *Project Manager* notifies the *Contractor* of the compensation event at the time of the event. He also instructs the *Contractor* to submit quotations, unless the event arises from a fault of the *Contractor* or quotations have already been submitted. The *Contractor* puts the instruction or changed decision into effect.

61.2 The *Project Manager* may instruct the *Contractor* to submit quotations for a proposed instruction or a proposed changed decision. The *Contractor* does not put a proposed instruction or a proposed changed decision into effect.

61.3 The *Contractor* notifies an event which has happened or which he expects to happen to the *Project Manager* as a compensation event if

- the *Contractor* believes that the event is a compensation event,
- it is less than two weeks since he became aware of the event and
- the *Project Manager* has not notified the event to the *Contractor*.

61.4 The Prices and the Completion Date are not changed if the *Project Manager* decides that an event notified by the *Contractor*

- arises from a fault of the *Contractor*,
- has not happened and is not expected to happen,
- has no effect upon Actual Cost or Completion or
- is not one of the compensation events stated in this contract.

If the *Project Manager* decides otherwise, he instructs the *Contractor* to submit quotations for the event. Within either

- one week of the *Contractor*'s notification or
- a longer period to which the *Contractor* has agreed

the *Project Manager* notifies his decision to the *Contractor* or instructs him to submit quotations.

61.5 If the *Project Manager* decides that the *Contractor* did not give an early warning of the event which an experienced contractor could have given, he notifies this decision to the *Contractor* when he instructs him to submit quotations.

61.6 If the *Project Manager* decides that the effects of a compensation event are too uncertain to be forecast reasonably, he states assumptions about the event in his instruction to the *Contractor* to submit quotations. Assessment of the event is based on these assumptions. If any of them is later found to have been wrong, the *Project Manager* notifies a correction.

61.7 A compensation event is not notified after the *defects date*.

Quotations for compensation events **62**

62.1 The *Project Manager* may instruct the *Contractor* to submit alternative quotations based upon different ways of dealing with the compensation event which are practicable. The *Contractor* submits the required quotations to the *Project Manager* and may submit quotations for other methods of dealing with the compensation event which he considers practicable.

62.2 Quotations for compensation events comprise proposed changes to the Prices and any delay to the Completion Date assessed by the *Contractor*. The *Contractor* submits details of his assessment with each quotation. If the programme for remaining work is affected by the compensation event, the *Contractor* includes a revised programme in his quotation showing the effect.

62.3 The *Contractor* submits quotations within three weeks of being instructed to do so by the *Project Manager*. The *Project Manager* replies within two weeks of the submission. His reply is

- an instruction to submit a revised quotation,
- an acceptance of a quotation,
- a notification that a proposed instruction or a proposed changed decision will not be given or
- a notification that he will be making his own assessment.

62.4 The *Project Manager* instructs the *Contractor* to submit a revised quotation only after explaining his reasons for doing so to the *Contractor*. The *Contractor* submits the revised quotation within three weeks of being instructed to do so.

62.5 The *Project Manager* extends the time allowed for

- the *Contractor* to submit quotations for a compensation event and
- the *Project Manager* to reply to a quotation

if the *Project Manager* and the *Contractor* agree to the extension before the submission or reply is due. The *Project Manager* notifies the extension that has been agreed to the *Contractor*.

Assessing compensation events **63**

63.1 The changes to the Prices are assessed as the effect of the compensation event upon

- the Actual Cost of the work already done,
- the forecast Actual Cost of the work not yet done and
- the resulting Fee.

63.2 If the effect of a compensation event is to reduce the total Actual Cost, the Prices are not reduced except as stated in this contract. If the effect of a compensation event is to reduce the total Actual Cost and the event is

- a change to the Works Information or
- a correction of an assumption stated by the *Project Manager* for assessing an earlier compensation event,

the Prices are reduced.

63.3 A delay to the Completion Date is assessed as the length of time that, due to the compensation event, planned Completion is later than planned Completion as shown on the Accepted Programme.

63.4 If the *Project Manager* has notified the *Contractor* of his decision that the *Contractor* did not give an early warning of a compensation event which an experienced contractor could have given, the event is assessed as if the *Contractor* had given early warning.

63.5 Assessment of the effect of a compensation event includes cost and time risk allowances for matters which have a significant chance of occurring and are at the *Contractor*'s risk under this contract.

63.6 Assessments are based upon the assumptions that the *Contractor* reacts competently and promptly to the compensation event, that the additional Actual Cost and time due to the event are reasonably incurred and that the Accepted Programme can be changed.

63.7 A compensation event which is an instruction to change the Works Information in order to resolve an ambiguity or inconsistency is assessed as follows. If Works Information provided by the *Employer* is changed, the effect of the compensation event is assessed as if the Prices and the Completion Date were for the interpretation most favourable to the *Contractor*. If Works Information provided by the *Contractor* is changed, the effect of the compensation event is assessed as if the Prices and the Completion Date were for the interpretation most favourable to the *Employer*.

The *Project Manager*'s assessments

64

64.1 The *Project Manager* assesses a compensation event
- if the *Contractor* has not submitted a required quotation and details of his assessment within the time allowed,
- if the *Project Manager* decides that the *Contractor* has not assessed the compensation event correctly in a quotation and he does not instruct the *Contractor* to submit a revised quotation,
- if, when the *Contractor* submits quotations for a compensation event, he has not submitted a programme which this contract requires him to submit or
- if when the *Contractor* submits quotations for a compensation event the *Project Manager* has not accepted the *Contractor*'s latest programme for one of the reasons stated in this contract.

64.2 The *Project Manager* assesses a compensation event using his own assessment of the programme for the remaining work if
- there is no Accepted Programme or
- the *Contractor* has not submitted a revised programme for acceptance as required by this contract.

64.3 The *Project Manager* notifies the *Contractor* of his assessment of a compensation event and gives him details of it within the period allowed for the *Contractor*'s submission of his quotation for the same event. This period starts when the need for the *Project Manager*'s assessment becomes apparent.

Implementing compensation events

65

65.1 The *Project Manager* implements each compensation event by notifying the *Contractor* of the quotation which he has accepted or of his own assessment. He implements the compensation event when he accepts a quotation or completes his own assessment or when the compensation event occurs, whichever is latest.

65.2 The assessment of a compensation event is not revised if a forecast upon which it is based is shown by later recorded information to have been wrong.

● **a new**
● **engineering contract**
● **document**

NOVEMBER 1995

● **the engineering**

● **and construction**

● **contract**

Addendum to take into account

THE HOUSING GRANTS, CONSTRUCTION AND REGENERATION ACT 1996 (PART II)

NEC Engineering and Construction Contract

ADDENDUM

to take into account

THE HOUSING GRANTS, CONSTRUCTION AND REGENERATION ACT 1996 (PART II)

© The Institution of Civil Engineers

The Institution of Civil Engineers has approved amendments produced by its NEC Panel to cover the introduction of the Housing Grants, Construction and Regeneration Act 1996 (Part II) for use with the NEC Engineering and Construction Contract in England, Wales, Scotland and Northern Ireland.

NOTES FOR GUIDANCE

Option Y(UK)2: The Housing Grants, Construction and Regeneration Act 1996

This option is prepared solely for use on contracts which are subject to the Housing Grants, Construction and Regeneration Act 1996 ("the Act"). The option should not be used in other circumstances.

If the contract is subject to the Act, this option is incorporated into the contract by making the following statement in the Contract Data:-

1. General   The *conditions of contract* are the core clauses for Options . . . . and Y(UK)2 (published by the ICE April 1998) of the second edition (November 1995) of the NEC Engineering and Construction Contract.

The two principles contained in this Act, which affect the NEC family of contracts, are those related to payment and adjudication. The definition of a "construction contract" in this Act is wide ranging and can be found in Section 104. It covers not only an agreement to carry out "construction operations" but also an agreement to provide professional services for a "construction operation".

The definition of a "construction operation" can be found in Section 105(1) of the Act. The operations and contracts that are not subject to the Act are defined in Sections 105(2) and 106. In the United Kingdom (England, Wales, Scotland and Northern Ireland), the Parties to a contract should consider carefully whether the operation is subject to the Act before proceeding. If the operation or contract is subject to the Act, it is intended that, by incorporating Option Y(UK)2 in to the contract, the provisions of the statutory Scheme for Construction Contracts do not become implied terms of the contract (S. 114(4)). Parties must be aware that it is not possible to contract out of a statutory requirement.

Clauses Y2.1 to 2.4 have been drafted with the intention of complying with Sections 109 to 113 and Clauses Y2.5 and 2.6 have been drafted with the intention of complying with Section 108 of the Act.

Y2.1   In the NEC family of contracts periods of time are usually measured in weeks thus avoiding complications of rest days and statutory holidays in different countries in which these contracts are used. The Act, however, defines most periods as a number of days. S.116(3) of the Act states that Christmas Day, Good Friday and bank holidays are excluded from any period specified in the Act. Where the time period associated with the Act is referred to, that period has been stated in days in Option Y(UK)2.

Y2.3   These additional clauses in Y(UK)2 are drafted to accommodate Sections 109 to 111 of the Act. The *Employer* is now required to give notice to the *Contractor* of the payment to be made, and the basis on which the calculation is made. This is achieved by stating that the *Project Manager* specifically carries out this function on behalf of the *Employer* The *Employer's* certificates may need to be changed to cover this point.

The Act uses very specific language about what and when "payments become due", when particular notices are issued and defining the "final date for payment". The latter applies to each certified payment and not just to the final payment "after Completion of the whole of the *works*". Provision has been made for a different payment period to be stated in the Contract Data.

Clause 56.1 sets out time periods and circumstances to meet the requirements of S. 110 (1) and 110(2) of the Act. S. 110(1)(a) requires an "adequate mechanism for determining what payments become due under the contract and when". This mechanism is provided by the *Project Manager's* certificate which is required to be issued by the date due which is 7 days after the assessment date. S. 110(1)(b) requires that there should be "a final date for payment in relation to any sum which becomes due". This is 28 days, or the period stated in the Contract Data, after the assessment date. The significance of the final date for payment is that if the *Employer* intends to withhold part of the amount due, he must give notice not later than a "prescribed period" ie 7 days before the final date for payment as indicated in S. 111 of the Act.

Y2.4   Under S.112 of the Act, where a sum due is not paid by the final date for payment and no effective notice to withhold payment has been given, the *Contractor* has a right to suspend performance. This right can only be exercised if the *Contractor* gives 7 days' notice of his intention. The right to suspend ceases when payment is made in full. Under S. 112(4) of the Act, the Completion Date is, in effect, delayed by the period of suspension. The effect of the additional clause 60.7 is to treat such suspension as a compensation event. Thus, in addition to the extra time, the *Contractor* is entitled to additional costs resulting from the suspension.

Y2.5   Like nearly all other forms of contract before the 1996 Act, the provisions in the NEC family of contracts for settling disputes do not comply with the Act. The purpose of Section 9 has always been to overcome where possible the causes of disputes and, in those cases where disputes may still arise, to facilitate their clear definition and early resolution. Hence this amendment replaces core clause 90 with new clauses which should comply with the Act. The intention of the new clauses is to retain the principles of the adjudication provisions in the ECC in managing disputes, and at the same time comply with the Act so that the fall-back "Scheme for Construction Contracts" does not apply.

The new clauses require a meeting to be held to discuss any matter of dissatisfaction, with a view to resolving the matter. If this procedure fails to resolve the matter, a dispute arises after which either Party can give notice of his intention to refer it to adjudication. The remaining procedure in the clause is similar to that in core clause 90.

Y2.6   Y(UK)2 clause 90 supersedes core clause 91.1 which is now deleted. The new clause 91.1 extends the procedure for a meeting to resolve a matter of dissatisfaction, to include a subcontractor, where the relevant matter is one which involves the subcontractor.

Construction Act - Payment Periods - April 1998
Engineering and Construction Contract

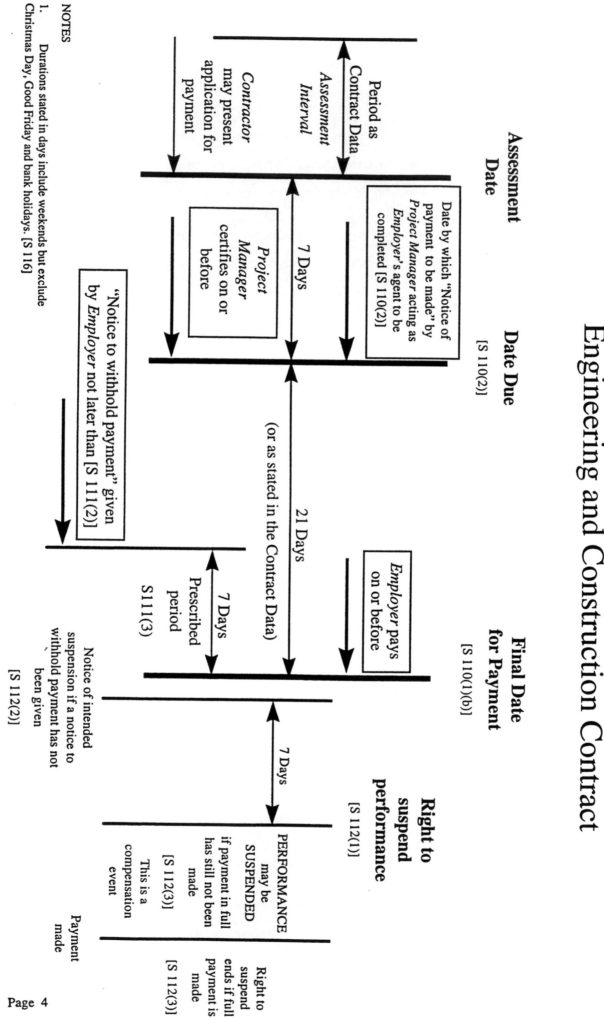

Assessment Date

Period as Contract Data

Assessment Interval

Contractor may present application for payment

Date by which "Notice of payment to be made" by *Project Manager* acting as *Employer's* agent to be completed [S 110(2)]

Date Due

[S 110(2)]

Project Manager certifies on or before

7 Days

(or as stated in the Contract Data)

21 Days

"Notice to withhold payment" given by *Employer* not later than [S 111(2)]

Employer pays on or before

Final Date for Payment

[S 110(1)(b)]

S111(3) Prescribed period

7 Days

Right to suspend performance

[S 112(1)]

Notice of intended suspension if a notice to withhold payment has not been given

[S 112(2)]

7 Days

PERFORMANCE may be SUSPENDED if payment in full has still not been made

[S 112(3)]

This is a compensation event

Right to suspend suspend ends if full payment is made

[S 112(3)]

Payment made

NOTES

1. Durations stated in days include weekends but exclude Christmas Day, Good Friday and bank holidays. [S 116]

Page 4

ADDENDUM

Option Y(UK)2: The Housing Grants, Construction and Regeneration Act 1996

Y2.1   In this Option

- the Act means The Housing Grants, Construction and Regeneration Act 1996 and
- periods of time stated in days are reckoned in accordance with Section 116 of the Act.

Y2.2   **Clause 51 is amended as follows:-**

Clause 51.1   the first sentence is deleted and replaced with the following sentence:-

"The *Project Manager* certifies a payment on or before the date on which a payment becomes due."

Clause 51.2   the first sentence is deleted and replaced with the following sentence:-

"Each certified payment is made on or before the final date for payment."

Y2.3   **The following clauses are added**

Dates for Payment   **56**

56.1   For the purpose of Sections 109 and 110 of the Act,

- the *Project Manager*'s certificate is the notice of payment from the *Employer* to the *Contractor* specifying the amount (if any) of the payment made or proposed to be made, and the basis on which that amount was calculated,

- the date on which a payment becomes due is seven days after the assessment date and

- the final date for payment is

    - twenty one days or
    - if a different period for payment is stated in the Contract Data, the period stated

    after the date on which the payment becomes due.

56.2   If the *Employer* intends to withhold payment after the final date for payment of a sum due under this contract, he notifies the *Contractor* not later than seven days (the prescribed period) before the final date for payment by specifying

- the amount proposed to be withheld and the ground

for withholding payment or
- if there is more than one ground, each ground and the amount attributable to it.

Y2.4   **The following is added to clause 60**

60.7   Suspension of performance is a compensation event if the *Contractor* exercises his right to suspend performance under the Act.

Y2.5   **Clause 90 is deleted and replaced by the following:**

Avoidance and settlement   **90**
of disputes   90.1   The Parties and the *Project Manager* follow this procedure for the avoidance and settlement of disputes.

90.2   If the *Contractor* is dissatisfied with an action or a failure to take action by the *Project Manager*, he notifies his dissatisfaction to the *Project Manager* no later than

- four weeks after he became aware of the action or
- four weeks after he became aware that the action had not been taken.

Within two weeks of such notification of dissatisfaction, the *Contractor* and the *Project Manager* attend a meeting to discuss and seek to resolve the matter.

90.3   If either Party is dissatisfied with any other matter, he notifies his dissatisfaction to the *Project Manager* and to the other Party no later than four weeks after he became aware of the matter. Within two weeks of such notification of dissatisfaction, the Parties and the *Project Manager* attend a meeting to discuss and seek to resolve the matter.

90.4   The Parties agree that no matter shall be a dispute unless a notice of dissatisfaction has been given and the matter has not been resolved within four weeks. The word dispute (which includes a difference) has that meaning.

90.5   Either Party may give notice to the other Party at any time of his intention to refer a dispute to adjudication. The notifying Party refers the dispute to the *Adjudicator* within seven days of the notice.

90.6   The Party referring the dispute to the *Adjudicator* includes with his submission information to be considered by the *Adjudicator*. Any further information from a Party to be considered by the *Adjudicator* is provided within fourteen days of referral.

90.7   Unless and until the *Adjudicator* has given his decision on the dispute, the Parties and the *Project Manager* proceed as if the action, failure to take action or other matters were not disputed.

90.8   The *Adjudicator* acts impartially. The *Adjudicator* may take the initiative in ascertaining the facts and the law.

90.9   The *Adjudicator* reaches a decision within twenty eight days of referral or such longer period as is agreed by the Parties after the dispute has been referred. The *Adjudicator* may extend the period of twenty eight days by up to fourteen days with the consent of the notifying Party.

90.10   The *Adjudicator* provides his reasons to the Parties and to the *Project Manager* with his decision.

90.11   The decision of the *Adjudicator* is binding until the dispute is finally determined by the *tribunal* or by agreement.

90.12   The *Adjudicator* is not liable for anything done or omitted in the discharge or purported discharge of his functions as adjudicator unless the act or omission is in bad faith and any employee or agent of the *Adjudicator* is similarly protected from liability.

Y2.6   **Clause 91 is amended as follows:-**

Side heading "**The adjudication**" is replaced with "**Combining procedures**"

Clause 91.1 is deleted and replaced by the following:-

91.1   If a matter causing dissatisfaction under or in connection with a subcontract is also a matter causing dissatisfaction under or in connection with this contract, the subcontractor may attend the meeting between the Parties and the *Project Manager* to discuss and seek to resolve the matter.

Clause 91.2   line 4   "settles" is replaced with "gives his decision on"

Y2.7   **Clause 92 is amended as follows:-**

Clause 92.1   line 1   "settles" is replaced with "gives his decision on"

Clause 92.2   line 6   "settle" is replaced with "decide on"

Clause 92.2   line 7   "had not been settled" is replaced with "a decision had not been given"

Y2.8   **Contract Data Part 1 - Optional statements**

The fifth optional statement is deleted and replaced by the following:-

"**If the period for payment is not twenty one days**

• The period within which payments are made is ..... days"

**THE INSTITUTION OF
CIVIL ENGINEERS**

65.3   The *Project Manager* includes the changes to the forecast amount of the Prices and the Completion Date in his notification to the *Contractor* implementing a compensation event.

65.5   The *Contractor* does not implement a subcontract compensation event until it has been agreed by the *Project Manager*.

7 Title

The *Employer*'s title to Equipment, Plant and Materials **70**

70.1 Whatever title the *Contractor* has to Equipment, Plant and Materials which is outside the Working Areas passes to the *Employer* if the *Supervisor* has marked it as for this contract.

70.2 Whatever title the *Contractor* has to Equipment, Plant and Materials passes to the *Employer* if it has been brought within the Working Areas. The title to Equipment, Plant and Materials passes back to the *Contractor* if it is removed from the Working Areas with the *Project Manager*'s permission.

Marking Equipment, Plant and Materials outside the Working Areas **71**

71.1 The *Supervisor* marks Eqiupment, Plant and Materials which are outside the Working Areas if

- this contract identifies them for payment and
- the *Contractor* has prepared them for marking as the Works Information requires.

Removing Equipment **72**

72.1 The *Contractor* removes Equipment from the Site when it is no longer needed unless the *Project Manager* allows it to be left in the *works*.

Objects and materials within the Site **73**

73.1 The *Contractor* has no title to an object of value or of historical or other interest within the Site. The *Contractor* notifies the *Project Manager* when such an object is found and the *Project Manager* instructs the *Contractor* how to deal with it. The *Contractor* does not move the object without instructions.

73.2 The *Contractor* has title to materials from excavation and demolition only as stated in the Works Information.

8 Risks and insurance

Employer's risks   **80**

80.1   The _Employer_'s risks are

- Claims, proceedings, compensation and costs payable which are due to

  - use or occupation of the Site by the _works_ or for the purpose of the _works_ which is the unavoidable result of the _works_,
  - negligence, breach of statutory duty or interference with any legal right by the _Employer_ or by any person employed by or contracted to him except the _Contractor_ or
  - a fault of the _Employer_ or a fault in his design.

- Loss of or damage to Plant and Materials supplied to the _Contractor_ by the _Employer_, or by Others on the _Employer_'s behalf, until the _Contractor_ has received and accepted them.

- Loss of or damage to the _works_, Plant and Materials due to

  - war, civil war, rebellion, revolution, insurrection, military or usurped power,
  - strikes, riots and civil commotion not confined to the _Contractor_'s employees,
  - radioactive contamination.

- Loss of or damage to the parts of the _works_ taken over by the _Employer_, except loss or damage occurring before the issue of the Defects Certificate which is due to

  - a Defect which existed at take over,
  - an event occurring before take over which was not itself an _Employer_'s risk or
  - the activities of the _Contractor_ on the Site after take over.

- Loss of or damage to the _works_ and any Equipment, Plant and Materials retained on the Site by the _Employer_ after a termination, except loss and damage due to the activities of the _Contractor_ on the Site after the termination.

- Additional _Employer_'s risks stated in the Contract Data.

The _Contractor_'s risks   **81**

81.1   From the _starting date_ until the Defects Certificate has been issued the risks which are not carried by the _Employer_ are carried by the _Contractor_.

Repairs   **82**

82.1   Until the Defects Certificate has been issued and unless otherwise instructed by the _Project Manager_ the _Contractor_ promptly replaces loss of and repairs damage to the _works_, Plant and Materials.

Indemnity   **83**

83.1   Each Party indemnifies the other against claims, proceedings, compensation and costs due to an event which is at his risk.

83.2 The liability of each Party to indemnify the other is reduced if events at the other Party's risk contributed to the claims, proceedings, compensation and costs. The reduction is in proportion to the extent that events which were at the other Party's risk contributed, taking into account each Party's responsibilities under this contract.

Insurance cover 84

84.1 The *Contractor* provides the insurances stated in the Insurance Table except any insurance which the *Employer* is to provide as stated in the Contract Data. The *Contractor* provides additional insurances as stated in the Contract Data.

84.2 The insurances are in the joint names of the Parties and provide cover for events which are at the *Contractor*'s risk from the *starting date* until the Defects Certificate has been issued.

INSURANCE TABLE

Insurance against	Minimum amount of cover or minimum limit of indemnity
Loss of or damage to the *works*, Plant and Materials.	The replacement cost, including the amount stated in the Contract Data for the replacement of any Plant and Materials provided by the *Employer*.
Loss of or damage to Equipment.	The replacement cost.
Liability for loss of or damage to property (except the *works*, Plant and Materials and Equipment) and liability for bodily injury to or death of a person (not an employee of the *Contractor*) caused by activity in connection with this contract.	The amount stated in the Contract Data for any one event with cross liability so that the insurance applies to the Parties separately.
Liability for death of or bodily injury to employees of the *Contractor* arising out of and in the course of their employment in connection with this contract.	The greater of the amount required by the applicable law and the amount stated in the Contract Data for any one event.

Insurance policies 85

85.1 The *Contractor* submits policies and certificates for the insurance which he is to provide to the *Project Manager* for acceptance before the *starting date* and afterwards as the *Project Manager* instructs. A reason for not accepting the policies and certificates is that they do not comply with this contract.

85.2 Insurance policies include a waiver by the insurers of their subrogation rights against directors and other employees of every insured except where there is fraud.

85.3 The Parties comply with the terms and conditions of the insurance policies.

85.4 Any amount not recovered from an insurer is borne by the *Employer* for events which are at his risk and by the *Contractor* for events which are at his risk.

If the *Contractor* does not **86**
insure 86.1 The *Employer* may insure a risk which this contract requires the *Contractor* to insure if the *Contractor* does not submit a required policy or certificate. The cost of this insurance to the *Employer* is paid by the *Contractor*.

Insurance by the *Employer* **87**

87.1 The *Project Manager* submits policies and certificates for insurances provided by the *Employer* to the *Contractor* for acceptance before the *starting date* and afterwards as the *Contractor* instructs. The *Contractor* accepts the policies and certificates if they comply with this contract.

87.2 The *Contractor*'s acceptance of an insurance policy or certificate provided by the *Employer* does not change the responsibility of the *Employer* to provide the insurances stated in the Contract Data.

87.3 The *Contractor* may insure a risk which this contract requires the *Employer* to insure if the *Employer* does not submit a required policy or certificate. The cost of this insurance to the *Contractor* is paid by the *Employer*.

9 Disputes and termination

Settlement of disputes **90**

90.1 Any dispute arising under or in connection with this contract is submitted to and settled by the *Adjudicator* as follows.

ADJUDICATION TABLE

Dispute about:	Which Party may submit it to the *Adjudicator*?	When may it be submitted to the *Adjudicator*?
An action of the *Project Manager* or the *Supervisor*	The *Contractor*	Between two and four weeks after the *Contractor*'s notification of the dispute to the *Project Manager*, the notification itself being made not more than four weeks after the *Contractor* becomes aware of the action
The *Project Manager* or *Supervisor* not having taken an action	The *Contractor*	Between two and four weeks after the *Contractor*'s notification of the dispute to the *Project Manager*, the notification itself being made not more than four weeks after the *Contractor* becomes aware that the action was not taken
Any other matter	Either Party	Between two and four weeks after notification of the dispute to the other Party and the *Project Manager*

90.2 The *Adjudicator* settles the dispute by notifying the Parties and the *Project Manager* of his decision together with his reasons within the time allowed by this contract. Unless and until there is such a settlement, the Parties and the *Project Manager* proceed as if the action, inaction or other matter disputed were not disputed. The decision is final and binding unless and until revised by the *tribunal*.

The adjudication **91**

91.1 The Party submitting the dispute to the *Adjudicator* includes with his submission information to be considered by the *Adjudicator*. Any further information from a Party to be considered by the *Adjudicator* is provided within four weeks from the submission. The *Adjudicator* notifies his decision within four weeks of the end of the period for providing information. The four week periods in this clause may be extended if requested by the *Adjudicator* in view of the nature of the dispute and agreed by the Parties.

91.2 If a matter disputed under or in connection with a subcontract is also a matter disputed under or in connection with this contract, the *Contractor* may submit the subcontract dispute to the *Adjudicator* at the same time as the main contract submission. The *Adjudicator* then settles the two disputes together and references to the Parties for the purposes of the dispute are interpreted as including the Subcontractor.

The *Adjudicator* 92

92.1   The *Adjudicator* settles the dispute as independent adjudicator and not as arbitrator. His decision is enforceable as a matter of contractual obligation between the Parties and not as an arbitral award. The *Adjudicator*'s powers include the power to review and revise any action or inaction of the *Project Manager* or *Supervisor* related to the dispute. Any communication between a Party and the *Adjudicator* is communicated also to the other Party. If the *Adjudicator*'s decision includes assessment of additional cost or delay caused to the *Contractor*, he makes his assessment in the same way as a compensation event is assessed.

92.2   If the *Adjudicator* resigns or is unable to act, the Parties choose a new adjudicator jointly. If the Parties have not chosen a new adjudicator jointly within four weeks of the *Adjudicator* resigning or becoming unable to act, a Party may ask the person stated in the Contract Data to choose a new adjudicator and the Parties accept his choice. The new adjudicator is appointed as *Adjudicator* under the NEC Adjudicator's Contract. He has power to settle disputes that were currently submitted to his predecessor but had not been settled at the time when his predecessor resigned or became unable to act. The date of his appointment is the date of submission of these disputes to him as *Adjudicator*.

Review by the *tribunal* 93

93.1   If after the *Adjudicator*

- notifies his decision or
- fails to do so

within the time provided by this contract a Party is dissatisfied, that Party notifies the other Party of his intention to refer the matter which he disputes to the *tribunal*. It is not referable to the *tribunal* unless the dissatisfied Party notifies his intention within four weeks of

- notification of the *Adjudicator*'s decision or
- the time provided by this contract for this notification if the *Adjudicator* fails to notify his decision within that time

whichever is the earlier. The *tribunal* proceedings are not started before Completion of the whole of the *works* or earlier termination.

93.2   The *tribunal* settles the dispute referred to it. Its powers include the power to review and revise any decision of the *Adjudicator* and any action or inaction of the *Project Manager* or the *Supervisor* related to the dispute. A Party is not limited in the *tribunal* proceedings to the information, evidence or arguments put to the *Adjudicator*.

Termination 94

94.1   If either Party wishes to terminate, he notifies the *Project Manager* giving details of his reason for terminating. The *Project Manager* issues a termination certificate promptly if the reason complies with this contract.

94.2   The *Contractor* may terminate only for a reason identified in the Termination Table. The *Employer* may terminate for any reason. The procedures followed and the amounts due on termination are in accordance with the Termination Table.

TERMINATION TABLE

Terminating Party	Reason	Procedure	Amount due
The *Employer*	A reason other than R1 – R21	P1 and P2	A1, A2 and A4
	R1 – R15, R19	P1, P2 and P3	A1 and A3
	R17, R18, R21	P1 and P3	A1, A2 and A5
The *Contractor*	R1 – R10, R16, R20	P1 and P4	A1, A2 and A4
	R17, R18, R21	P1 and P4	A1, A2 and A5

94.3 The procedures for termination are implemented immediately after the *Project Manager* has issued a termination certificate.

94.4 Within thirteen weeks of termination, the *Project Manager* certifies a final payment to or from the *Contractor* which is the *Project Manager*'s assessment of the amount due on termination less the total of previous payments.

94.5 After a termination certificate has been issued, the *Contractor* does no further work necessary to complete the *works*.

Reasons for termination **95**

95.1 Either Party may terminate if the other Party has done one of the following or its equivalent.

(a) If the other Party is an individual and has

- presented his petition for bankruptcy (R1),
- had a bankruptcy order made against him (R2),
- had a receiver appointed over his assets (R3) or
- made an arrangement with his creditors (R4).

(b) If the other Party is a company or partnership and has

- had a winding-up order made against it (R5),
- had a provisional liquidator appointed to it (R6),
- passed a resolution for winding-up (other than in order to amalgamate or reconstruct) (R9),
- had an administration order made against it (R8),
- had a receiver, receiver and manager, or administrative receiver appointed over the whole or a substantial part of its undertaking or assets (R7) or
- made an arrangement with its creditors (R10).

95.2 The *Employer* may terminate if the *Project Manager* has notified that the *Contractor* has defaulted in one of the following ways and not put the default right within four weeks of the notification.

- Substantially failed to comply with his obligations (R11).
- Not provided a bond or guarantee which this contract requires (R12).
- Appointed a Subcontractor for substantial work before the *Project Manager* has accepted the Subcontractor (R13).

95.3 The *Employer* may terminate if the *Project Manager* has notified that the *Contractor* has defaulted in one of the following ways and not stopped defaulting within four weeks of the notification.

- Substantially hindered the *Employer* or Others (R14).
- Substantially broken a health or safety regulation (R15).

95.4 The *Contractor* may terminate if the *Employer* has not paid an amount certified by the *Project Manager* within thirteen weeks of the date of the certificate (R16).

95.5 Either Party may terminate if

- war or radioactive contamination has substantially affected the *Contractor*'s work for 26 weeks (R17) or
- the Parties have been released under the law from further performance of the whole of this contract (R18).

95.6 If the *Project Manager* has instructed the *Contractor* to stop or not to start any substantial work or all work and an instruction allowing the work to restart or start has not been given within thirteen weeks,

- the *Employer* may terminate if the instruction was due to a default by the *Contractor* (R19),
- the *Contractor* may terminate if the instruction was due to a default by the *Employer* (R20) and
- either Party may terminate if the instruction was due to any other reason (R21).

Procedures on termination   **96**

96.1 On termination, the *Employer* may complete the *works* himself or employ other people to do so and may use any Plant and Materials to which he has title (P1).

96.2 The procedure on termination also includes one or more of the following as set out in the Termination Table.

P2   The *Employer* may instruct the *Contractor* to leave the Site, remove any Equipment, Plant and Materials from the Site and assign the benefit of any subcontract or other contract related to performance of this contract to the *Employer*.

P3   The *Employer* may use any Equipment to which he has title.

P4   The *Contractor* leaves the Working Areas and removes the Equipment.

Payment on termination **97**

97.1 The amount due on termination includes (A1)

- an amount due assessed as for normal payments,
- the Actual Cost for Plant and Materials

  - within the Working Areas or
  - to which the *Employer* has title and of which the *Contractor* has to accept delivery,

- other Actual Cost reasonably incurred in expectation of completing the whole of the *works*,
- any amounts retained by the *Employer* and
- a deduction of any unrepaid balance of an advanced payment.

97.2 The amount due on termination also includes one or more of the following as set out in the Termination Table.

A2 The forecast Actual Cost of removing the Equipment.

A3 A deduction of the forecast of the additional cost to the *Employer* of completing the the whole of the *works*.

A4 The *fee percentage* applied to any excess of the first forecast of the Actual Cost for the *works* over the Price for Work Done to Date less the Fee.

A5 Half of A4.

SECONDARY OPTION CLAUSES

Option G : Performance bond

Performance bond G1

G1.1   The *Contractor* gives the Employer a performance bond, provided by a bank or insurer which the *Project Manager* has accepted, for the amount stated in the Contract Data and in the form set out in the Works Information. A reason for not accepting the bank or insurer is that its commercial position is not strong enough to carry the bond. If the bond was not given by the Contract Date, it is given to the *Employer* within four weeks of the Contract Date.

Option H : Parent company guarantee

Parent company guarantee H1

H1.1   If a parent company owns the *Contractor*, the *Contractor* gives to the *Employer* a guarantee by the parent company of the *Contractor*'s performance in the form set out in the Works Information. If the guarantee was not given by the Contract Date, it is given to the *Employer* within four weeks of the Contract Date.

Option J : Advanced payment to the *Contractor*

Advanced payment J1

J1.1   The *Employer* makes an advanced payment to the *Contractor* of the amount stated in the Contract Data.

J1.2   The advanced payment is made either within four weeks of the Contract Date or, if an advanced payment bond is required, within four weeks of the later of

- the Contract Date and
- the date when the *Employer* receives the advanced payment bond.

The advanced payment bond is issued by a bank or insurer which the *Project Manager* has accepted. A reason for not accepting the proposed bank or insurer is that its commercial position is not strong enough to carry the bond. The bond is for the amount of the advanced payment and in the form set out in the Works Information. Delay in making the advanced payment is a compensation event.

J1.3   The advanced payment is repaid to the *Employer* by the *Contractor* in instalments of the amount stated in the Contract Data. An instalment is included in each amount due assessed after the period stated in the Contract Data has passed until the advanced payment has been repaid.

Option L : Sectional Completion

Sectional Completion **L1**

L1.1   In these *conditions of contract*, unless stated as the whole of the *works*, each reference and clause relevant to

- the *works*,
- Completion and
- Completion Date

applies, as the case may be, to either the whole of the *works* or any *section* of the *works*.

Option M : Limitation of the *Contractor*'s liability for his design to reasonable skill and care

The *Contractor*'s design **M1**

M1.1   The *Contractor* is not liable for Defects in the *works* due to his design so far as he proves that he used reasonable skill and care to ensure that it complied with the Works Information.

Option Q : Bonus for early Completion

Bonus for early **Q1**
Completion Q1.1   The *Contractor* is paid a bonus calculated at the rate stated in the Contract Data for each day from the earlier of

- Completion and
- the date on which the *Employer* takes over the *works*

until the Completion Date.

Option R : Delay damages

Delay damages **R1**

R1.1   The *Contractor* pays delay damages at the rate stated in the Contract Data from the Completion Date for each day until the earlier of

- Completion and
- the date on which the *Employer* takes over the *works*.

R1.2   If the Completion Date is changed to a later date after delay damages have been paid, the *Employer* repays the overpayment of damages with interest. Interest is assessed from the date of payment to the date of repayment and the date of repayment is an assessment date.

Option S : Low performance damages

Low performance damages   S1

S1.1   If a Defect included in the Defects Certificate shows low performance with respect to a performance level stated in the Contract Data, the *Contractor* pays the amount of low performance damages stated in the Contract Data.

Option T : Changes in the law

Changes in the law   T1

T1.1   A change in the law of the country in which the Site is located is a compensation event if it occurs after the Contract Date. The *Project Manager* may notify the *Contractor* of a compensation event for a change in the law and instruct him to submit quotations. If the effect of a compensation event which is a change in the law is to reduce the total Actual Cost, the Prices are reduced.

Option U : The Construction (Design and Management) Regulations 1994 (to be used for contracts in UK)

The CDM Regulations   U1
1994   U1.1   A delay to the work or additional or changed work caused by application of The Construction (Design and Management) Regulations 1994 is a compensation event if an experienced contractor could not reasonably be expected to have foreseen it.

Option V : Trust Fund

Defined terms   V1

V1.1   (1) The Trust Fund is a fund held and administered by the *Trustees*.

(2) The Trust Deed is a deed between the *Employer* and the *Trustees* which contains the provisions for administering the Trust Fund. Terms defined in this contract have the same meaning in the Trust Deed.

(3) The Initial Value of the Trust Fund is an amount which is the total of the Prices at the Contract Date multiplied by 1.5 and divided by the number of months in the period between the Contract Date and the Completion Date.

(4) Insolvency of an individual occurs when that individual has

- presented his petition for bankruptcy,
- had a bankruptcy order made against him,
- had a receiver appointed over his assets or
- made an arrangement with his creditors.

(5) Insolvency of a company occurs when it has

- had a winding-up order made against it,
- had a provisional liquidator appointed to it,
- passed a resolution for winding-up (other than in order to amalgamate or reconstruct),
- had an administration order made against it,
- had a receiver, receiver and manager, or administrative receiver appointed over the whole or a substantial part of its undertaking or assets or
- made an arrangement with its creditors.

(6) The Beneficiaries are the *Contractor* and

- Subcontractors,
- suppliers of the *Contractor*,
- subcontractors of whatever tier of a Subcontractor and
- suppliers of whatever tier of a Subcontractor or of his subcontractors

who are employed to Provide the Works.

(7) A Trust Payment is a payment made by the *Trustees* out of the Trust Fund.

Trust Fund V2

V2.1   The *Employer* establishes the Trust Fund within one week of the Contract Date.

V2.2   The Trust Fund is established

- by the *Employer* making a payment to the *Trustees* equal to the Initial Value or
- by the *Employer* providing the *Trustees* with a guarantee of the Initial Value, payable to the *Trustees* on their first written demand, given by a bank or other financial institution acceptable to the *Trustees* or,
- if the *Employer* is a Government department or other public authority in the United Kingdom, by the *Employer* entering into irrevocable undertakings with the *Contractor* and the *Trustees* to pay the *Trustees* promptly on demand such amounts as they request for

  - Trust Payments and
  - their fees and expenses for administering the Trust Fund.

V2.3   The *Contractor* informs his suppliers and his Subcontractors of the terms of the Trust Deed and of the appointment of the *Trustees*. He arranges that Subcontractors ensure that their suppliers and subcontractors, of whatever tier, are also informed.

Trust Deed **V3**

V3.1 The Trust Fund is administered by the *Trustees* in accordance with the Trust Deed. The Trust Deed includes the following provisions.

(1) If a Beneficiary satisfies the *Trustees*

- that he has not received all or part of a payment properly due to him under his contract relating to the *works* which was unpaid at the time of the Insolvency and
- that the reason for the failure to pay is the Insolvency of the party which should have made the payment

the *Trustees* may at their discretion make a Trust Payment to the Beneficiary of an amount not exceeding the value of the payment which he has not received.

(2) If a Beneficiary subsequently receives a payment from another party, in respect of which a Trust Payment has been made, the Beneficiary passes on that payment to the *Trustees* (up to the value of the Trust Payment). Before making a Trust Payment the *Trustees* may require from a Beneficiary either an assignment of rights or an undertaking with respect to that payment in a form acceptable to them.

(3) The *Trustees* have discretion to decide the amount and timing of every Trust Payment. They may make a Trust Payment on account or withold a Trust Payment until they have assessed the total amount of debts owing to a Beneficiary arising out of an Insolvency. They may take into account any claims (including claims by way of set-off) which the party suffering from Insolvency may have against the Beneficiary as well as the likely ability of the liquidator or other administrator of the insolvent party to meet the claims of unsecured creditors from funds in his hands.

(4) If the Trust Fund was established by a payment, the *Employer* maintains the Trust Fund at the Initial Value. If the Trust Fund was established by a guarantor, the *Employer* ensures that the guarantor maintains the Trust Fund at the Initial Value. The *Trustees* notify the *Employer* or the guarantor within one week of making a Trust Payment and the *Employer* or the guarantor restores the Trust Fund to the Initial Value within two weeks of the notification.

(5) After the *Trustees* have made all Trust Payments, any amount in the Trust Fund (including any accrued interest) is paid by the *Trustees* to the *Employer*. If a guarantee has been provided, it is returned to the guarantor. The *Trustees* do not pay claims from Beneficiaries which they receive after the Defects Certificate has been issued.

(6) The *Employer* pays the *Trustees* their fees and expenses for administering the Trust Fund.

(7) The *Trustees* may engage professional consultants to help them with the administration of the Trust Fund and may make Trust Payments for their fees and expenses.

(8) The *Trustees* hold the Trust Fund on an interest-bearing bank account.

Option Z : Additional conditions of contract

Additional conditions of **Z1**
contract Z1.1 The additional conditions of contract stated in the Contract Data are part of this contract.

CONTRACT DATA

Part one – Data provided by the *Employer*

Statements given in all contracts

1. General

- The *conditions of contract* are the core clauses and the clauses for Options . . . . of the second edition (1995) of the NEC Engineering and Construction Contract.

- The *works* are

  . . . .

- The *Employer* is

  Name . . . .

  Address . . . .

  . . . .

- The *Project Manager* is

  Name . . . .

  Address . . . .

  . . . .

- The *Supervisor* is

  Name . . . .

  Address . . . .

  . . . .

- The *Adjudicator* is

  Name . . . .

  Address . . . .

  . . . .

- The Works Information is in

  . . . .

  . . . .

  . . . .

  . . . .

- The Site Information is in

  . . . .

  . . . .

  . . . .

  . . . .

- The *boundaries of the site* are . . . .

- The *language of this contract* is . . . .

- The *law of the contract* is the law of . . . .

- The *period for reply* to a communication is . . . . .weeks

2. The *Contractor*'s main responsibilities

- The *Contractor*'s liability for Defects due to his design that are not listed on the Defects Certificate is limited to . . . .

3. Time

- The *starting date* is . . . .

- The *possession dates* are

Part of the Site	Date
1	. . . .
2	. . . .
3	. . . .

- The *Contractor* submits revised programmes at intervals no longer than

. . . . weeks

4. Testing and Defects

- The *defects date* is . . . . weeks after Completion of the whole of the *works*

- The *defect correction period* is . . . . weeks

5. Payment

- The *currency of this contract* is the . . . .

- The *assessment interval* is . . . . weeks (not more than five)

- The *interest rate* is . . . . % per annum (not less than 2) above the . . . .

rate of the . . . . bank

6. Compensation events

- The place where weather is to be recorded is

. . . .

- The *weather measurements* to be recorded for each calendar month are

  - the cumulative rainfall (mm)
  - the number of days with rainfall more than 5 mm
  - the number of days with minimum air temperature less than 0 degrees Celsius
  - the number of days with snow lying at . . . . hours GMT

  and these measurements:

  . . . .

  . . . .

  . . . .

- The *weather data* are the records of past *weather measurements* for each calendar month which were recorded at . . . .

  and which are available from . . . .

  . . . .

Where no recorded data are available

- Assumed values for the ten year return *weather data* for each *weather measurement* for each calendar month are:

  . . . .

  . . . .

  . . . .

  . . . .

8. Risks and insurance

- The amount of the minimum limit of indemnity for insurance in respect of loss of or damage to property (except the *works*, Plant and Materials and Equipment) and liability for bodily injury to or death of a person (not an employee of the *Contractor*) due to activity in connection with this contract for any one event is . . . .

  . . . .

- The amount of the minimum limit of indemnity for insurance in respect of death of or bodily injury to employees of the *Contractor* arising out of and in the course of their employment in connection with this contract is . . . .

  . . . .

9. Disputes and termination

- The person who will choose a new adjudicator if the Parties cannot agree a choice is

  . . . .

  . . . .

- The *tribunal* is . . . .

  . . . .

Optional statements

If the *tribunal* is arbitration

- The arbitration procedure is . . . .

If the *Employer* has decided the *completion date* for the whole of the *works*

- The *completion date* for the whole of the *works* is . . . .

If the *Employer* is not willing to take over the *works* before the Completion Date

- The *Employer* is not willing to take over the *works* before the Completion Date.

If no programme is identified in part two of the Contract Data

- The *Contractor* is to submit a first programme for acceptance within . . . . weeks of the Contract Date.

If the period for payment is not three weeks

- The period within which payments are made is . . . . weeks

If there are additional compensation events

- These are compensation events

    1 . . . .

    2 . . . .

    3 . . . .

If there are additional *Employer*'s risks

- These are additional *Employer*'s risks

    1 . . . .

    2 . . . .

    3 . . . .

If the *Employer* is to provide Plant and Materials

- The insurance against loss of or damage to the *works*, Plant and Materials is to include cover for Plant and Materials provided by the *Employer* for an amount of . . . .

    . . . .

If the *Employer* is to provide any of the insurances stated in the Insurance Table

- The *Employer* provides these insurances from the Insurance Table

    1. Insurance against . . . .

    Cover/indemnity is . . . .

    The deductibles are . . . .

    2. Insurance against . . . .

    Cover/indemnity is . . . .

    The deductibles are . . . .

    3. Insurance against . . . .

    Cover/indemnity is . . . .

    The deductibles are . . . .

If additional insurances are to be provided

- The *Employer* provides these additional insurances

    1. Insurance against . . . .

    Cover/indemnity is . . . .

    The deductibles are . . . .

    2. Insurance against . . . .

    Cover/indemnity is . . . .

    The deductibles are . . . .

3. Insurance against . . . .

Cover/indemnity is . . . .

The deductibles are . . . .

- The *Contractor* provides these additional insurances

1. Insurance against . . . .

Cover/indemnity is . . . .

2. Insurance against . . . .

Cover/indemnity is . . . .

3. Insurance against . . . .

Cover/indemnity is . . . .

- **The *Contractor* prepares forecasts of Actual Cost for the *works* at intervals no longer than. . . . . weeks**
- **The *exchange rates* are those published in . . . . on . . . . (date)**

If Option G is used

- The amount of the performance bond is . . . .

If Option J is used

- The amount of the advanced payment is . . . .
- The *Contractor* repays the instalments in assessments starting not less than . . . . weeks after the Contract Date.
- The instalments are . . . .

. . . .

(either an amount or a percentage of the payment otherwise due)

- An advanced payment bond <u>is/is not</u> required.

If Option L is used

- The *completion date* for each *section* of the *works* is

Section	Description	*Completion date*
1	. . . .	. . . .
2	. . . .	. . . .
3	. . . .	. . . .
4	. . . .	. . . .
5	. . . .	. . . .

If Options L and Q are used together

- The bonuses for the *sections* of the *works* are

Section	Description	Amount per day
1	. . . .	. . . .
2	. . . .	. . . .
3	. . . .	. . . .
4	. . . .	. . . .
5	. . . .	. . . .

If Options L and R are used together

- Delay damages for the *sections* of the *works* are

Section	Description	Amount per day
1	. . . .	. . . .
2	. . . .	. . . .
3	. . . .	. . . .
4	. . . .	. . . .
5	. . . .	. . . .

If Option Q is used

- The bonus for the whole of the *works* is . . . . per day

If Option R is used (whether or not Option L is also used)

- Delay damages for the whole of the *works* are . . . . per day

If Option S is used

- The amounts for low performance damages are

Amount	Performance level
. . . .	for . . . .
. . . .	for . . . .
. . . .	for . . . .
. . . .	for . . . .

If Option V is used

- The *Trustees* are

Name . . . .

Address . . . .

Name . . . .

Address . . . .

If Option Z is used

- The additional conditions of contract are . . . .

. . . .

Part two - Data provided by the *Contractor*

Statements given in all contracts

- The *Contractor* is

  Name . . . .

  Address . . . .

  . . . .

- The *fee percentage* is . . . . %

- The *working areas* are the Site and . . . .

- The key people are

  (1) Name . . . .

  Job . . . .

  Responsibilities . . . .

  . . . .

  Qualifications . . . .

  Experience . . . .

  . . . .

  (2) Name . . . .

  Job . . . .

  Responsibilities . . . .

  . . . .

  Qualifications . . . .

  Experience . . . .

  . . . .

Optional statements

If the *Contractor* is to provide Works Information for his design

- The Works Information for the *Contractor*'s design is in

  . . . .

  . . . .

  . . . .

  . . . .

  . . . .

If a programme is to be identified in the Contract Data

- The programme identified in the Contract Data is . . . .

If the *Contractor* is to decide the *completion date* for the whole of the *works*

- The *completion date* for the whole of the *works* is . . . .

NEC ENGINEERING AND CONSTRUCTION CONTRACT

Index by clause numbers (option clauses are indicated by their letters)